Preface: Learn How Invisible Energy Rel_____es__ ___ _____ Nature re

This book is a gift to you and is meant to be read by anyone of any age. If someone is young and doesn't understand the message, my hope is that someone older will take the time to read it and explain it to them. Far too few people talk about nature as you will read in Give To Nature and Nature Will Give To You. It is up to all of us if we want to find the KEY, a word that is used as a hint or to find an answer to something. What are your eyes and ears paying attention to? Do you understand the difference between right and wrong?

There will be many events in your day-to-day life that will test you. You are here to transform into a person that knows there are principles that cannot be ignored. We are in the school of life to learn and get it right. It is about value for all life. My hope for you is that when reading Give To Nature and Nature Will Give To You, it will show you new and different ways to think and behave. Remember, everyone has a choice. Another hope is that you'll find your CARE deep inside you. You are very powerful with a BIG IMAGINATION. Good luck finding your KEY!

Growing in strength, knowledge & consciousness.
Love, Mother Earth

Table of Contents

Thoughts & Attention

Nature's Law of Mentalism

Mentalism

The All is MIND. The Universe is **MENTAL.** Our thoughts and imagination can lead to creating what we get and experience on Earth.

What is he thinking? →

MANIFESTATION

We can **MANIFEST** in our minds
bad or uncomfortable things
into our physical life.

Or

We can **MANIFEST**
fun things like tree houses.

READING KNOWLEDGE

Helps us Find the  which ↗

Helps Unlock
(Understand)

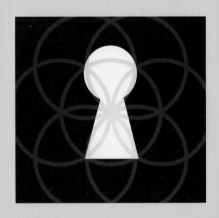

Information

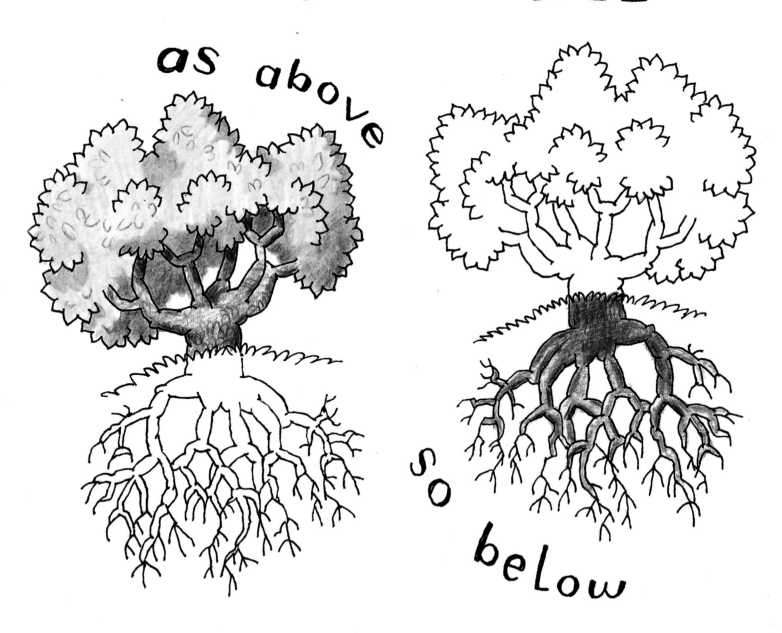

CORRESPONDENCE

Everything in **NATURE** is a mirror
or a reflection of what is going
on inside of us.

Metamorphosis (Met-a-mor-pho-sis)

From Caterpillar to Butterfly

(takes 28-38 days)

Nature's law of Correspondence is like a mirror that shows the stages of our human life that are similar to the life of a butterfly.

NATURE'S LAW OF
VIBRATION

VIBRATION

Everything is in motion.
Nothing is at rest.

The **ENERGY** we put out is
the energy we receive.

The little boy beating a drum
sends vibrations through the
Universe just as the girl that
is standing still.

Seed Germination

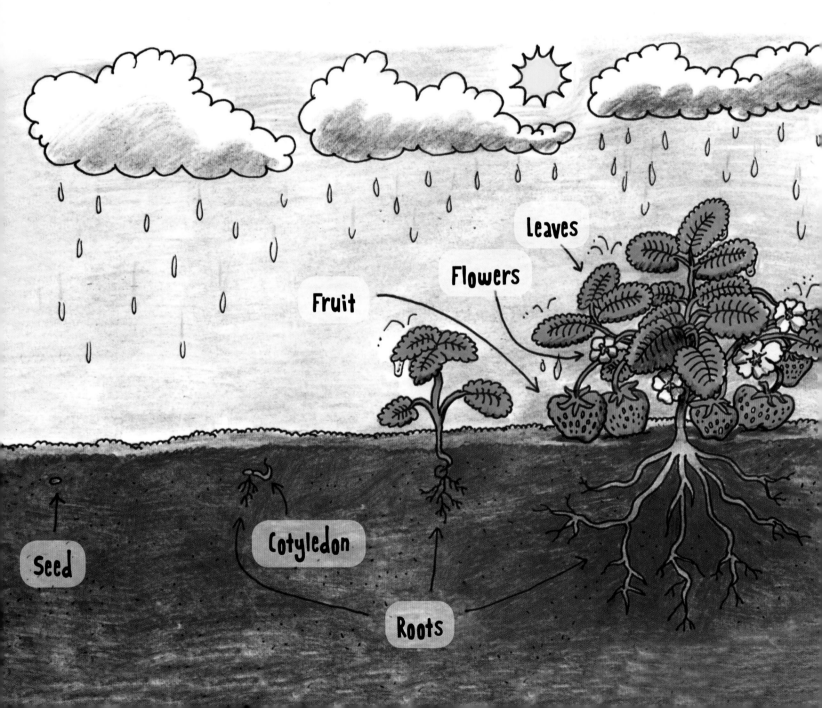

A GROWING SEED

Seed germination is how a
seed grows into a plant.

The life of a plant can grow
and develop just like
our consciousness.

SHARING IS CARING

SELFISH people only care about themselves and what they get. They do **NOT CARE** about the thoughts and feelings of other people or animals.

BEHAVIOR

Making the **CONSCIOUS** choice takes time to learn. You can control your behavior and no one else should be blamed. You and you alone are responsible for your actions.

Why am I CONNECTED to the whole UNIVERSE?

What is the difference between RIGHT and WRONG?

Why do I need to QUESTION things?

Why do I need KNOWLEDGE?

Good Parenting

TIME & ATTENTION

Children learn from the behaviors they see and the attitudes and conversations they hear. Also, they learn by how they are valued and treated at home.

CONSCIOUSNESS

It's about knowing what is going on in our mind, body, and spirit. It's also being aware of what is happening in and around us.

RHYTHM

Everything in nature is always moving like a pendulum – like the energy of the swing to the left will be the same as the energy of the swing to the right. There is always an action and reaction, a rising and a sinking. Night follows day, and day follows night.

FORCE OF GRAVITY

Nature's law holds everything
together and does not
require your belief.
It just is.

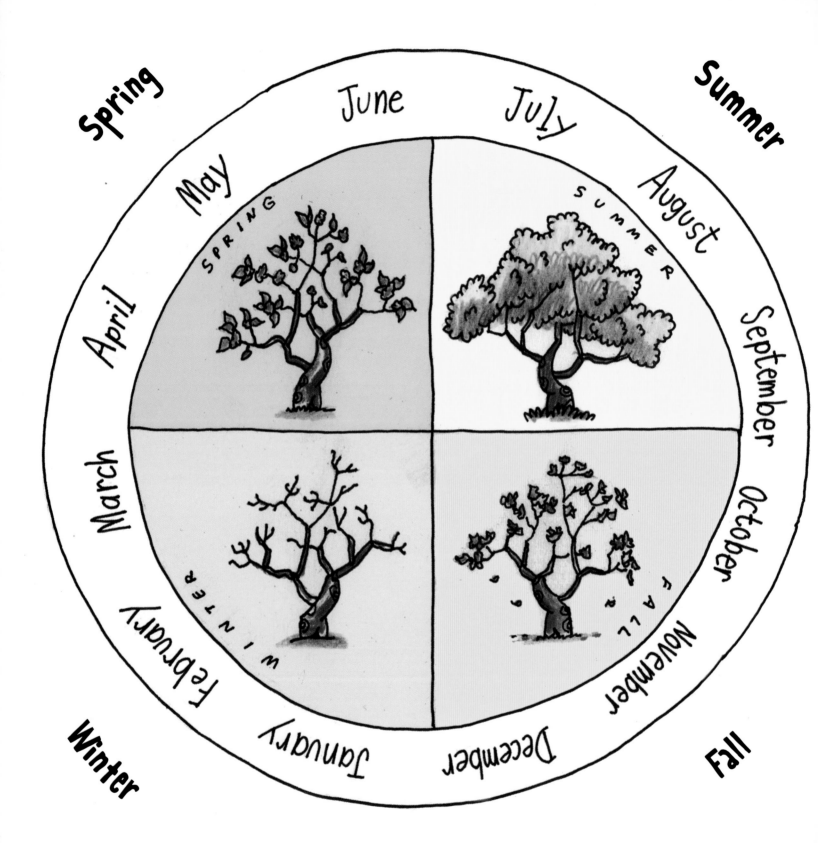

THE SEASONS OF THE SUN

(Northern Hemisphere)

The cycle, the circle or wheel of life, is a symbol showing you the seasons of the sun.

Ether (Energy)

Invisible

Earth   Air   Fire   Water

5 ELEMENTS
OF NATURE

These symbols show you
the energy that relates
to each element.

CARING

Take care of all things in nature and nature will take care of you.

NATURE'S LAW
OF POLARITY

LIGHT

COLD

POLARITY

Everything is DUAL,
everything has poles,
everything has its pair
of opposites.

DARK

HOT

The North Star
(POLARIS)

All stars revolve around this star every night.

Bring KNOWLEDGE to the INFORMATION to UNLOCK the UNIVERSE

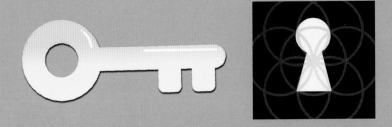

(Fill in the blank)

Truth is 1. _____ _____ _____.

To be 2. _____ is to be aware of our thoughts, feelings, actions, and surroundings.

(See answers at bottom of page)

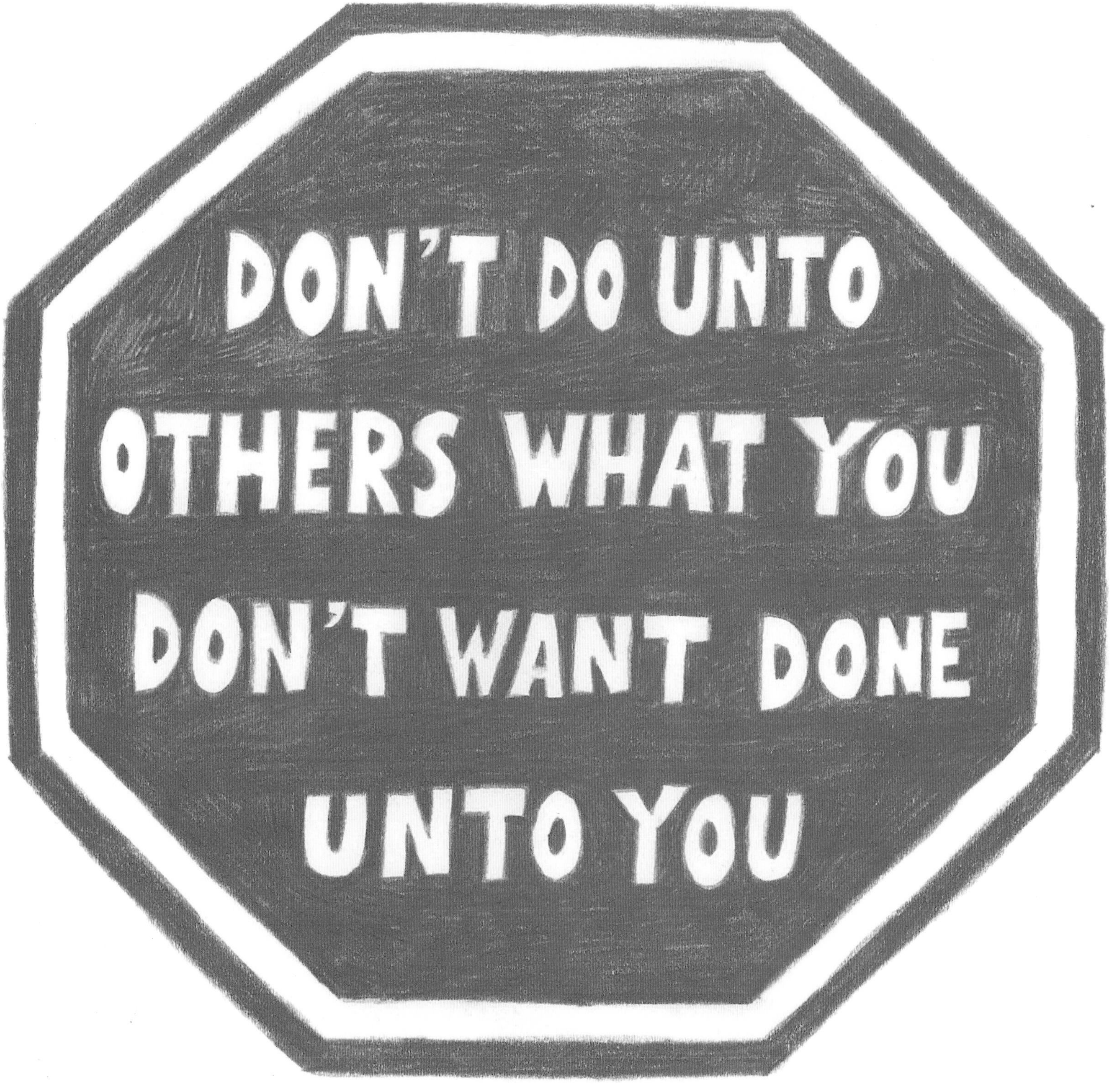
DON'T DO UNTO
OTHERS WHAT YOU
DON'T WANT DONE
UNTO YOU

GOLDEN RULE

Do unto others as you would
have them do unto you.

CAUSE AND

Nature's Law of Cause and Effect helps us understand and know the world that we create together. There's always a consequence for our behavior. This is sometimes called karma.

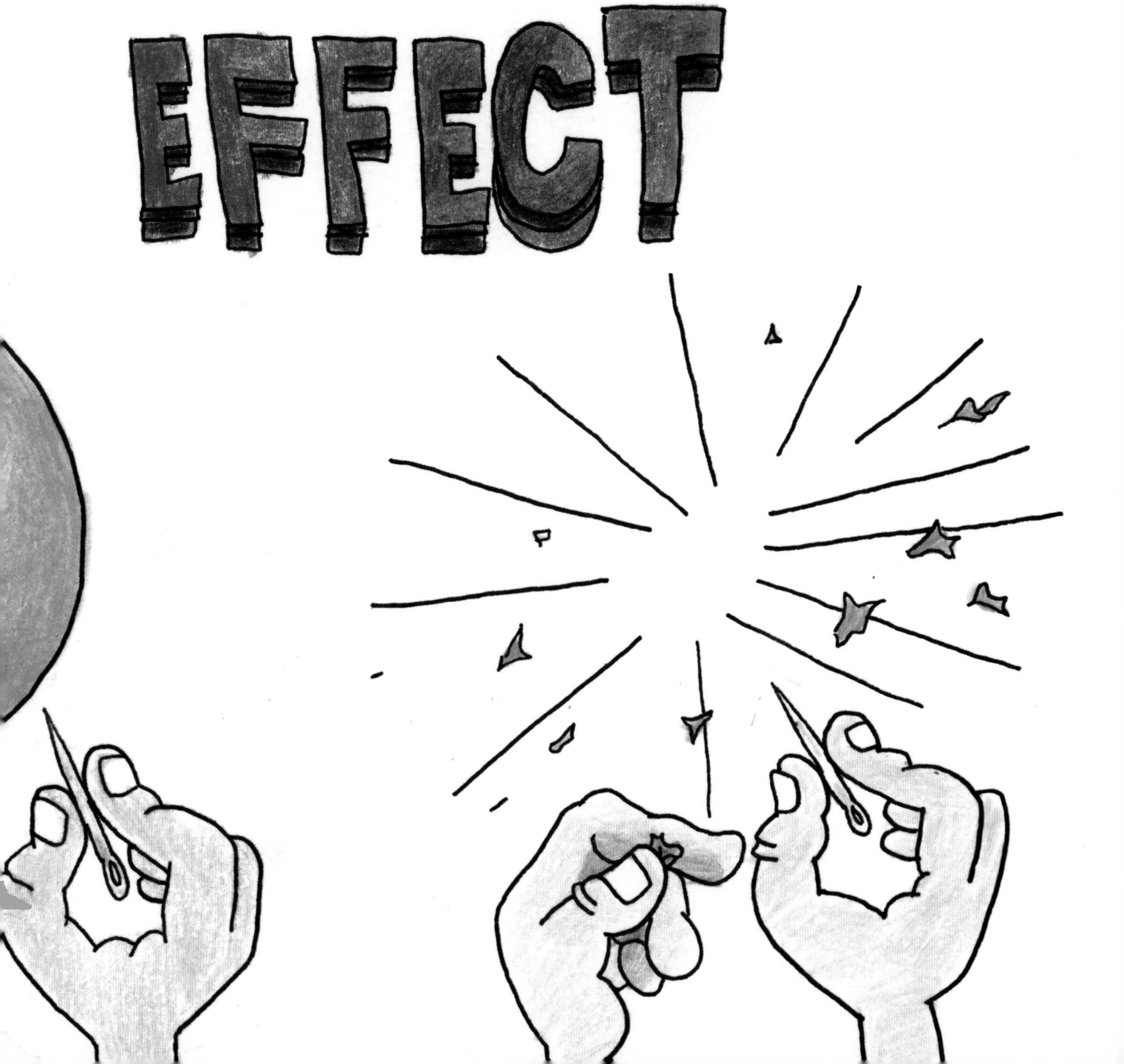
EFFECT

STEALING

Taking anything that doesn't belong to you is WRONG.

LYING

It is wrong to let someone
else take the blame for your behavior.

It is right to admit when we make
a mistake and take responsibility
for anything that causes harm
to someone, even a dog.

VIOLENCE VS. SELF-DEFENSE

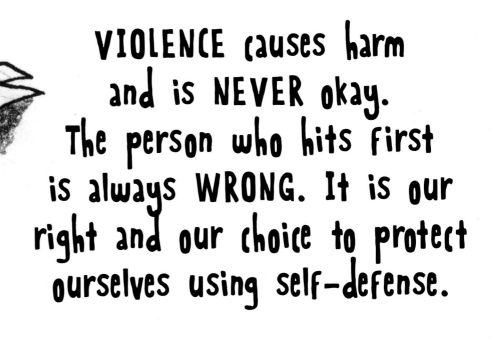

VIOLENCE causes harm and is NEVER okay. The person who hits first is always WRONG. It is our right and our choice to protect ourselves using self-defense.

When you play with fire, don't cry when you get burned.

CONSEQUENCES

Every action has a reaction.
If you do anything dangerous,
don't be surprised
if you get hurt.

NATURE'S LAW OF GENDER

Non-Physical Self (Spiritual)

GENDER

Everything in the Universe has a male and female energy to it.

TRUTH

TRUTH is that which IS. It's what has happened and what is happening.

When we don't want to see or hear TRUTH, it is because we are afraid to be responsible for what we know.

YOU are the:

YOU are the force that can grow.

Look inside the Seed of Life and you will see the vibrational force that will help you find your true nature. The journey will be measured by how much you CARE.

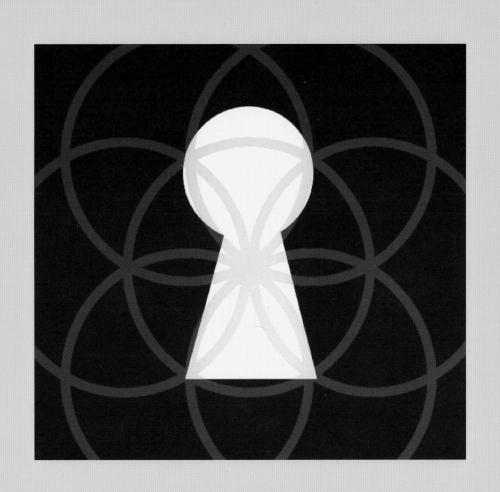

THE SEED OF LIFE

The Seed of Life is formed

from a relationship of 6 circles around one.

In fact, 6 circles will ALWAYS fit

exactly around a 7th circle of the same size.

It shows 7 days of creation.